· PARRAGON ·

3-D MASKS

KV-398-521

WILD ANIMALS

Model designs by Pat Doyle
Colour artworks by Blackjacks
Other artworks by Graham Osborne
Text by Karen Farrington

Wild Animals

It is always a joy to see animals in the wild. Even if we cannot always witness in person the antics of bear cubs in remote forests of North America or the thrilling spectacle of whales rearing out of the sea, there are books and television documentaries which give us a grandstand view. It is vital, however, that we do not take wild animals for granted.

What animals are wild?

We define animals as wild if we do not control their breeding and producing young. Horses, budgerigars and hamsters are tame or domesticated whereas snakes, lions and kangaroos are wild. Some animals we are familiar with are also considered wild – pigeons, grey squirrels and moorland ponies. But you will not see many animals that are wild, even if you live in the countryside. For wild animals like to avoid us. They know that humans can seriously damage their health.

Wild Animals at Risk

Animals are not always the victims of deliberate action. Centuries ago, as new and different countries were discovered, explorers introduced animals to lands where they did not naturally live. The newcomers often left native animals to starve. One example is the ancient giant tortoises of the Galapagos Islands which were left to go hungry when vegetation-eating goats arrived on the scene.

But there are also many animals that have suffered greatly becasue of the deliberate actions of humans. Whales are hunted for their meat and oils, which are made into soap. Over-hunting has taken all too many

quaggas, a type of zebra, was seen in 1884. There is a long list of animal species which have lost their fight for survival and an even longer list of animals which are close to doing so.

Conserving Wild Animals

Animals like the American red wolf can only be seen in zoos. Fortunately, enough people woke up in time to the threat which loomed for wild animals and acted to save them.

Arabian oryxes were hunted to the brink of extinction. Luckily, there were enough of these horned antelopes in zoos to breed in a carefully run programme. Stocks of them are now being released back into their native desert homes.

species, especially the blue and fin whales, to the brink of extinction. Despite attempts to bring in an international ban on whaling, the number of blue whales has sunk to an all-time low of only 1,500.

If animals are not successfully protected, some species will become extinct. That means the breed is wiped out forever. The dodo, a hook-beaked, flight-less bird, became extinct on the island of Mauritius in 1680. The last

There have been other success stories, too. Thanks to increased international co-operation there have been crackdowns on poachers and trading in the products from illegally killed animals.

Once it was the height of chic to wear a fur coat. Now the protests against the slaughter of animals for their coats has swayed public opinion against fur and as a result fewer animals are hunted.

Animal Habitats of the World

Animal Habitats

The world is divided into different *habitats*, that is, the places where animals live. The nature of a particular habitat depends on weather conditions, which determine the kinds of plants and animals that can live there. Some of the major habitats of the world are described on these pages.

Tundra

The northern and southernmost tips of the world, the Arctic and the Antarctic, are very tough places to live. In winter the temperature can fall to 60°C below freezing, and ice blocks four metrès thick float on the sea. The land is covered with a thick layer of ice and snow, making it very hard for plants and trees to survive. This bleak landscape is called *tundra*, and its inhabitants include seals, penguins, reindeer and polar bears.

Temperate Forest

These are the forests found in low-lying areas with mild winters and plentiful rainfall. They are found in central and western Europe, and parts of the USA.

In Europe the forests are made up mainly of trees that shed their leaves in winter, such as oak and ash, providing a rich compost for the forest floor.

Many animals make their home in temperate forests, including woodpecker, fox, squirrel and brown bear.

Tropical Rain Forest

Jungle, or tropical rain forest, is found in areas close to the equator (an imaginary line which runs around the middle of the globe). Parts of Central Africa, South America and South-East Asia are covered in rain forest.

Temperatures are high and rain falls throughout the year, producing a hot and steamy atmosphere ideal for thousands of different species of plants and animals. Rain forest is usually made up of three dense layers: a lower layer of trees 5-15 metres (16-50 ft) high, a middle layer 15-25 metres (50-80 ft) high, and a top layer of the tallest trees reaching heights of 40 metres (130 ft) above the ground.

All sorts of animals live in these forests around the world, including huge numbers of insects, tree frogs, jaguars, tigers, orang utans and parrots.

Savanna Grasslands

A climate known as savanna is found in a band between the tropics of Cancer and Capricorn (two imaginary lines which you can see on a map of the world). This band includes large parts of Africa, India, South America, China and northern Australia.

For most of the year temperatures are high. Each year the rainy season comes, often causing massive floods. During the long dry season the hot sun drys up the water and withers trees and plants.

Vegetation is a mixture of grasses, small plants and scattered trees, which provide food and shelter for many sorts of animals including lions, rhino, elephant, zebra, crocodile and giraffe.

Oceans

Two-thirds of the earth is covered by sea. At its bottom is a mysterious dark world, with huge unexplored mountains and sheer valleys many kilometres deep.

The ocean is home to scores of fish and other wildlife, including species which have never been seen by humans. Some, like jellyfish, sponge and coral, have existed for hundreds of millions of years. The world's largest mammal, the blue whale, which grows to lengths of 27 metres (88 ft) and weighs up to 152 tonnes (150 tons), is found in oceans throughout the world.

Wild Animal Superstars

The Brown Bear

Children who take a teddy bear to bed may think twice about getting too friendly with a real bear. Even if the cubs look cuddly, they are strong and extremely dangerous.

With large, flat feet and a short tail, bears are covered with a warm, shaggy coat of fur. Many of them are vegetarian, standing up on their hind legs to forage in bushes and trees for the tenderest shoots. In addition, they eat nuts, berries and mushrooms. You may already know from reading A. A. Milne's *Winnie the Pooh* stories that bears also like honey and happily raid the nests of bees to get it.

There are many different types of brown bear. Their size and colour varies from region to region, from near black to grey.

The Kodiak brown bear, a ferocious grizzly bear which lives in North America, is the largest living carnivore (meat-eater), growing up to 2.8 metres (9 ft) in height and weighing up to 760 kilograms (1,675 lbs).

During the harsh winter months brown bears hibernate in their dens – which are secluded underground hollows lined with leaves to keep them warm.

Apart from humans, the only other enemy of the brown bear is another brown bear.

The Rhinoceros

The plight of the rhino is a very sad story indeed. Once they were common and there were plenty of different types. In fact, the largest land mammal ever was a rhino which was more than 11 metres (36 lbs) long and 5.4 metres (18 ft) high. Now there are only five types left: the white, black, Indian, Sumatran and Javan.

Most have two horns made out of keratin, the same material that our hair and nails are made from. Only the Indian rhino has a single horn. Their dark skin is thick and virtually hair-free and they have large hooves.

All are protected from hunting and every type except the white is in real danger of dying out completely.

Rhinos are solitary creatures. Perhaps their best friends are birds, particularly the white cattle egrets which perch on their backs pecking at insects. Both benefit from this relationship with the egret finding a ready supply of food and the rhino finding relief from troublesome bugs.

Rhinos are particularly fond of wallowing in mud which helps to cool and cleanse them.

White rhinos are the largest of the species reaching two metres (6.5 ft) in height and weighing 3.5 tonnes (3.5 tons). The smallest is the Sumatran rhino which is just 1.5 metres (5 ft) at the shoulder and weighing about 750 kilograms (1,650 lbs).

The Crocodile

There is nothing cute or appealing about crocodiles. The sight of two beady eyes peering out of a tropical swamp is enough to give anyone the shivers. Yet these reptiles deserve our care and attention just as much as any other creature.

For a start, they are, along with alligators, perhaps the only living descendants of the dinosaurs. Nobody is sure what killed off the dinosaurs 65 million years ago. Look at pictures of some of the prehistoric creatures that once ruled the Earth and notice how today's crocodiles and alligators resemble them. They have been on Earth in one form or another for millions of years and have earned a place here.

Yet people have hunted them for their skins in order to make top fashion handbags and shoes. Many crocodiles and alligators live in national parks and are now protected to ensure their survival.

Crocodiles have a more pointed snout than alligators and fewer teeth. When their mouths are closed, the fourth tooth of the lower jaw still sticks up menacingly between its lips. This has given them the reputation of having an evil grin. Crocodiles can swim in water or run on land. They can even run only their two back legs – just like the cartoon crocodiles.

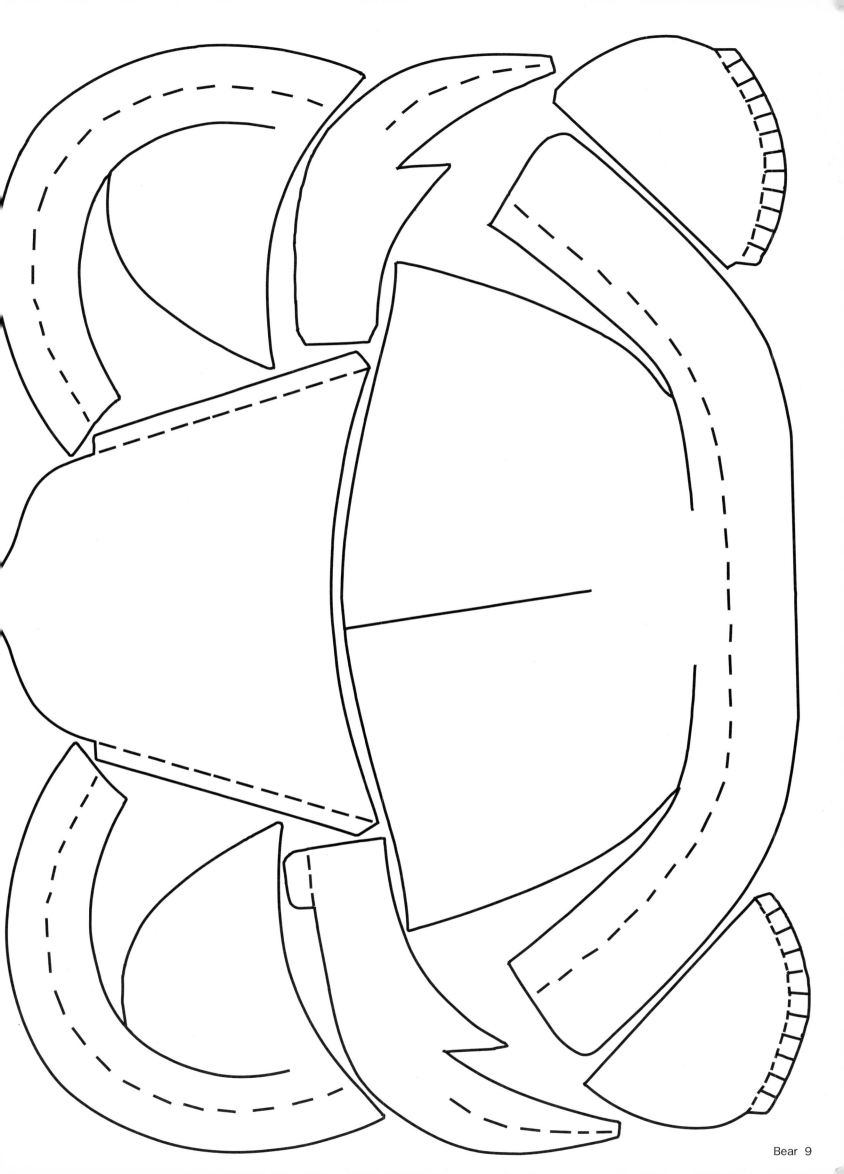

Bear 9

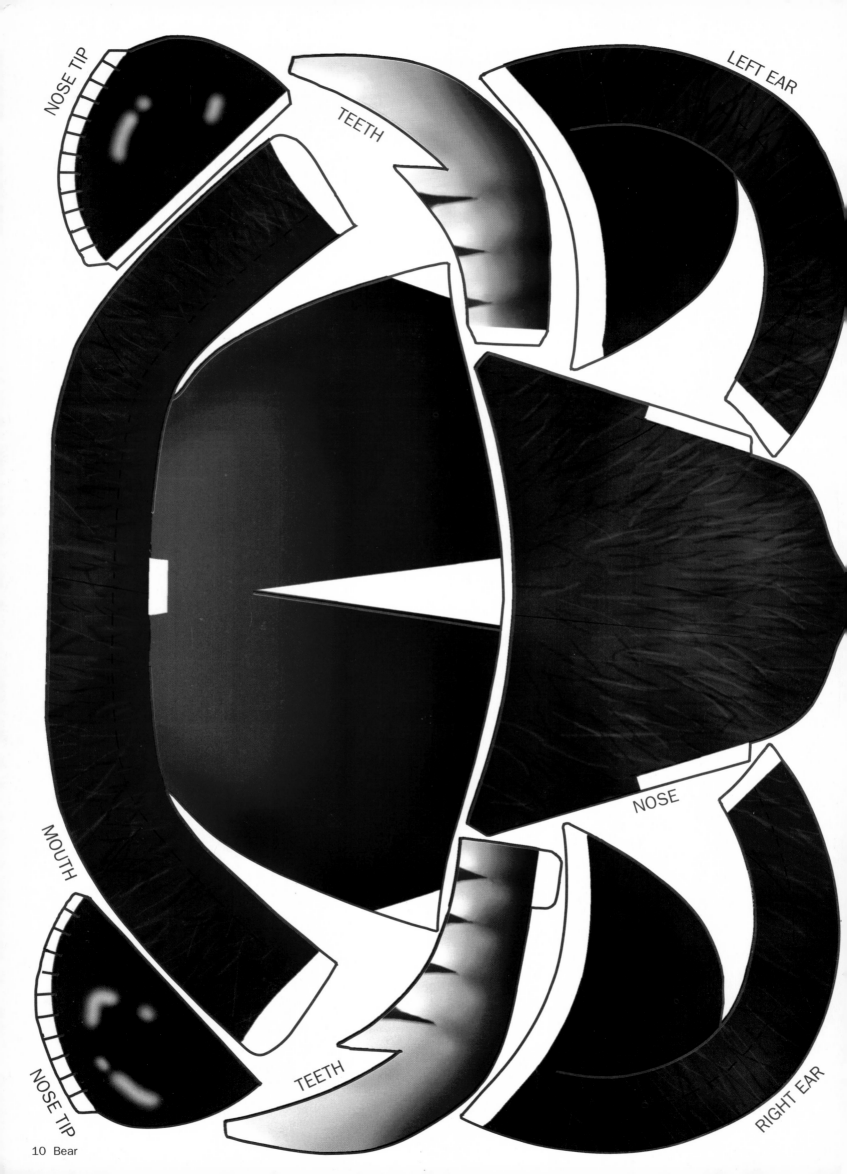

NOSE TIP

TEETH

LEFT EAR

MOUTH

NOSE

TEETH

NOSE TIP

RIGHT EAR

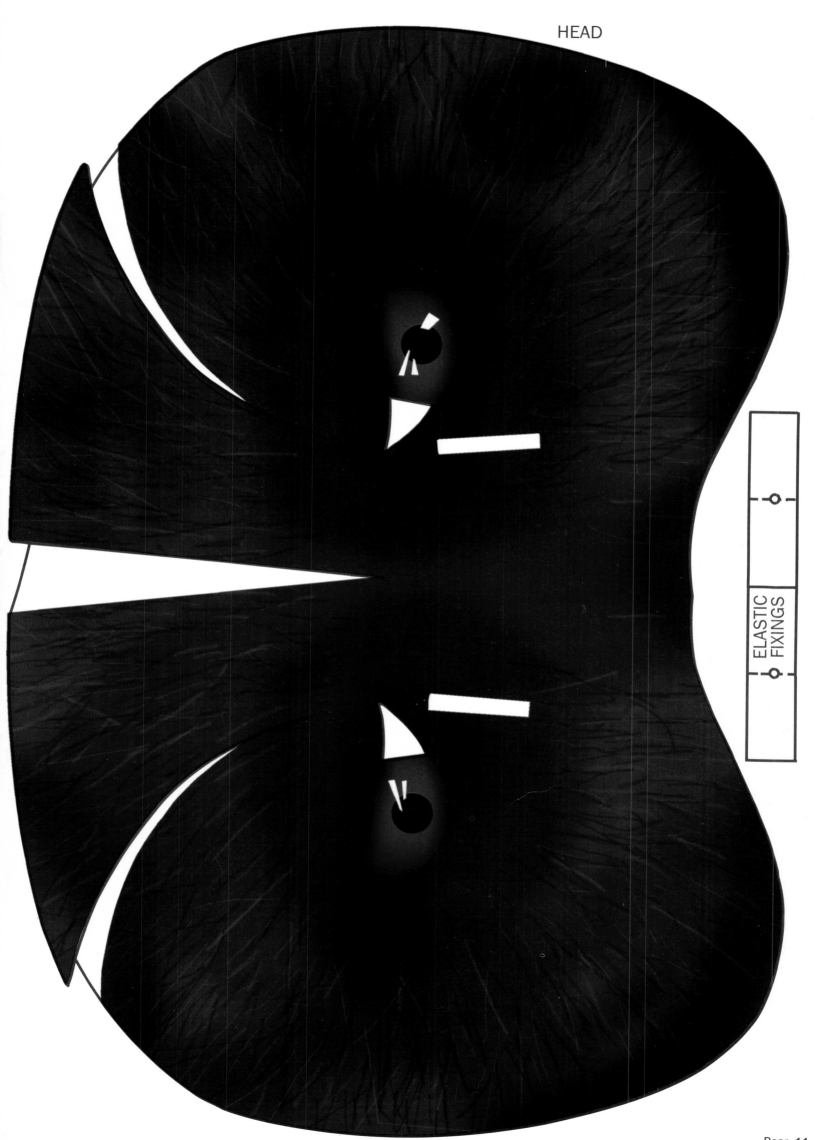

ELASTIC
FIXINGS

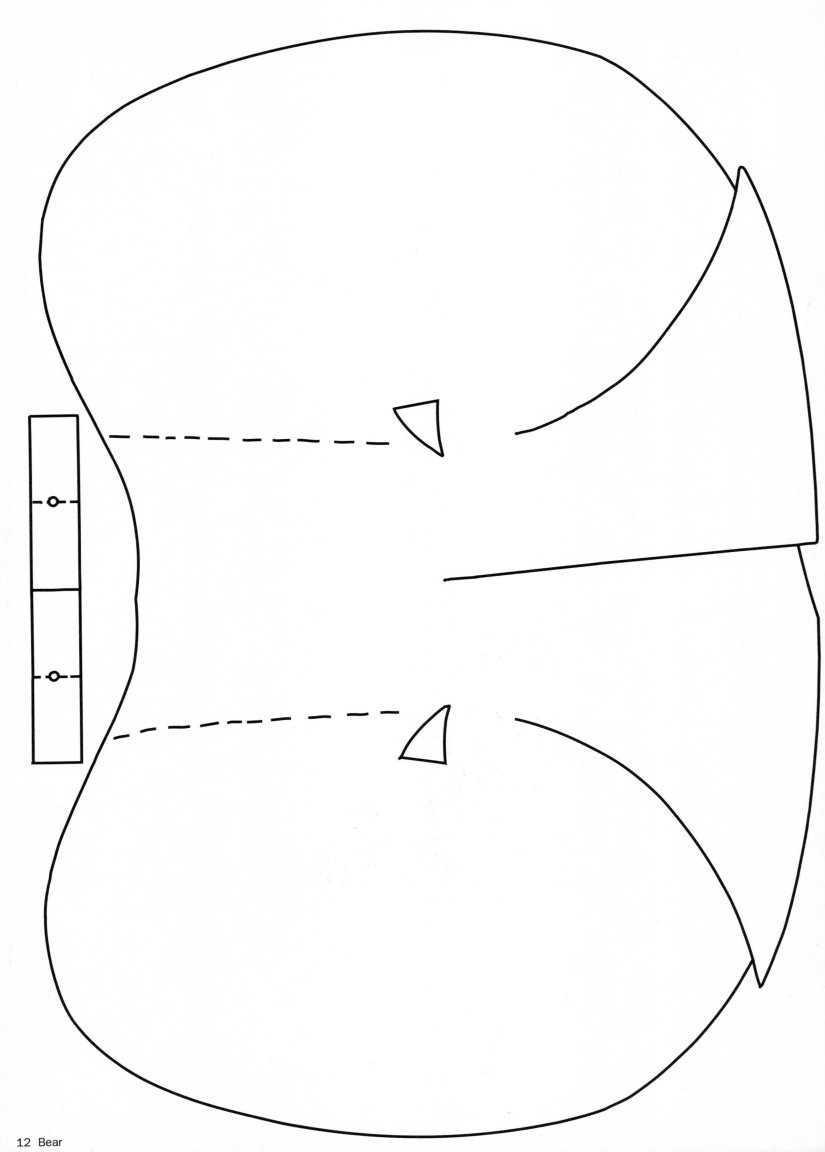

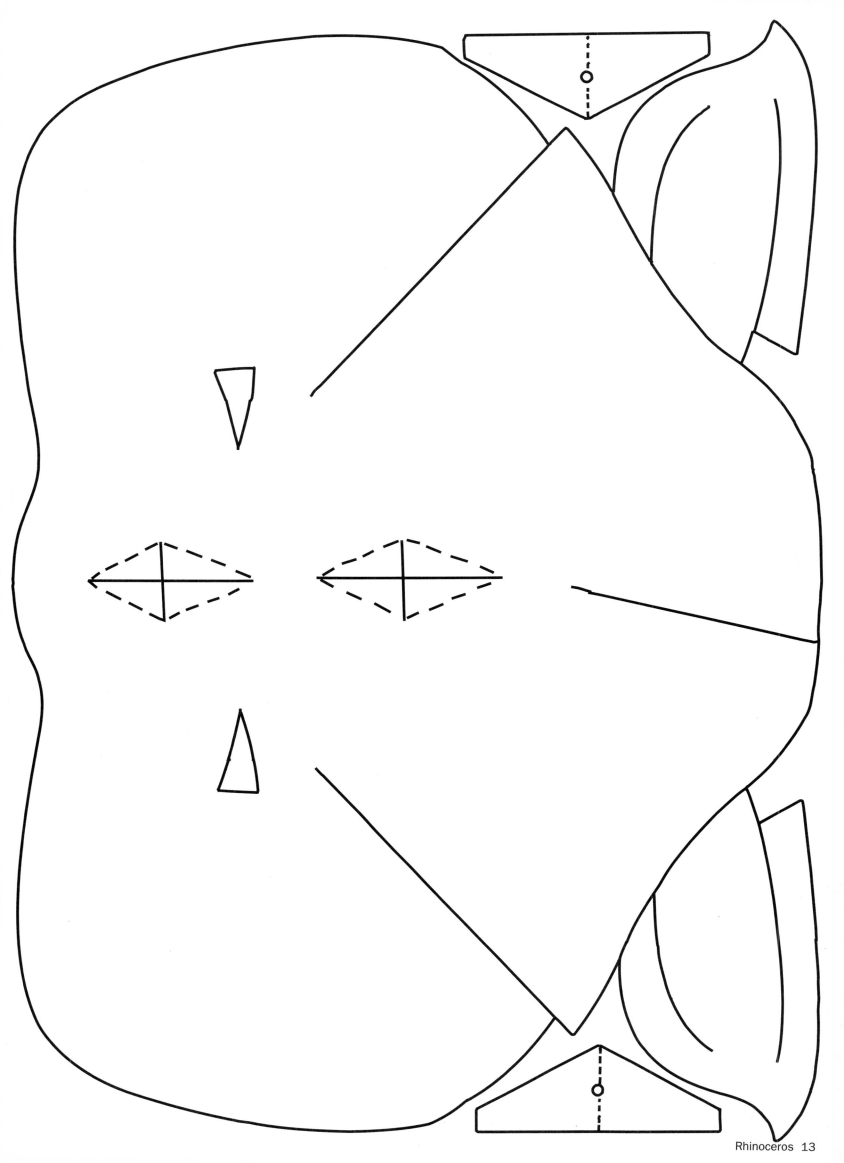

Rhinoceros 13

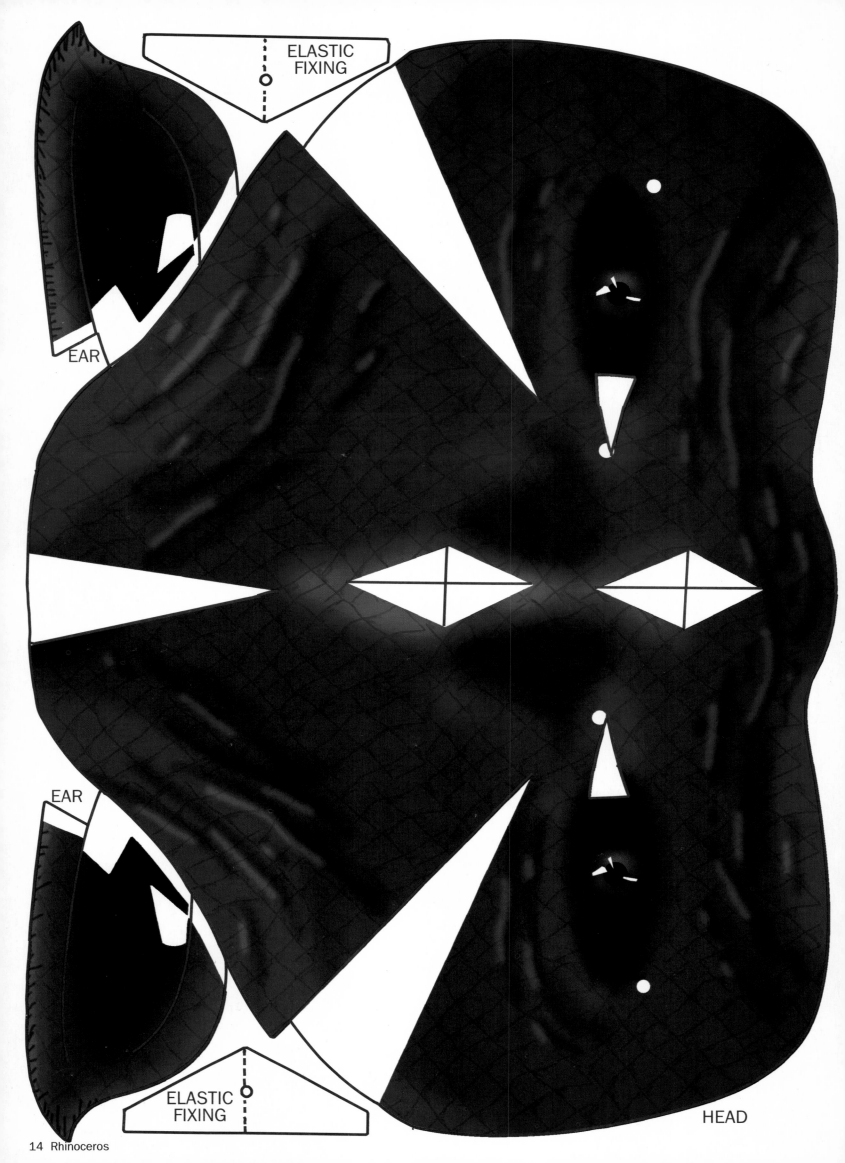

ELASTIC
FIXING

EAR

EAR

ELASTIC
FIXING

HEAD

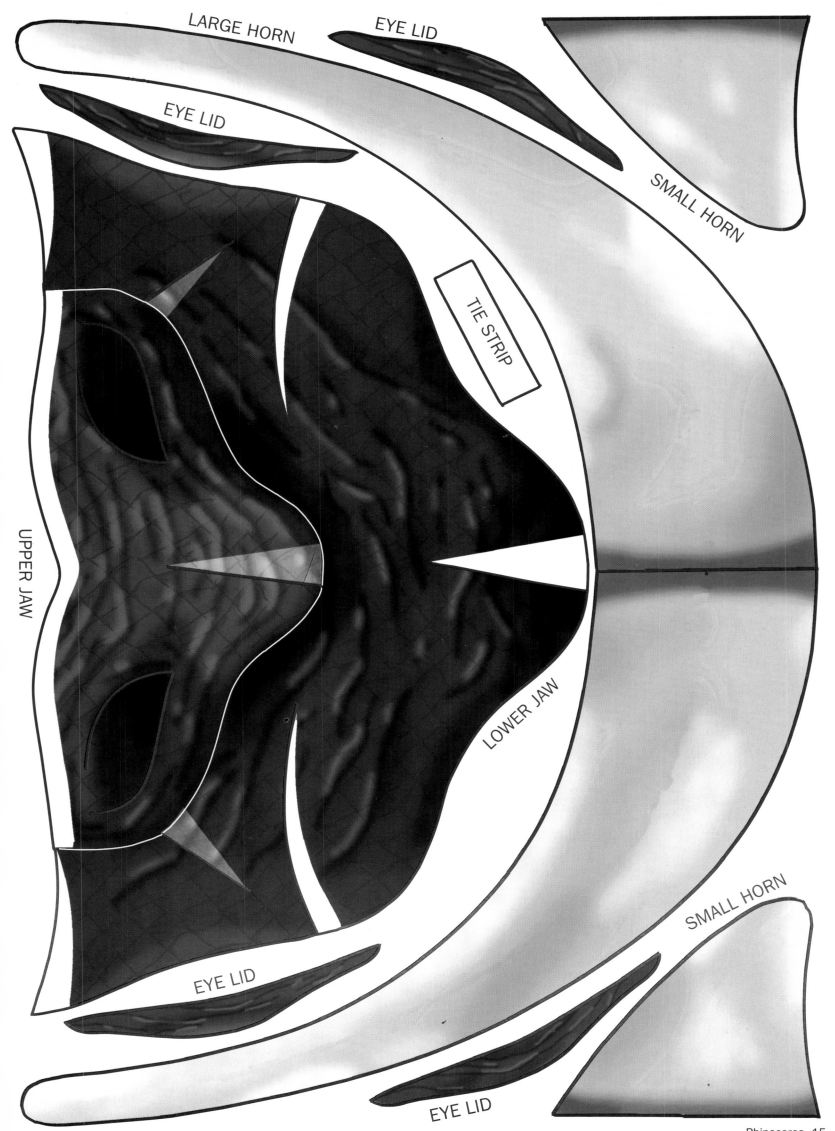

LARGE HORN

EYE LID

EYE LID

SMALL HORN

TIE STRIP

UPPER JAW

LOWER JAW

SMALL HORN

EYE LID

EYE LID

EYE LID

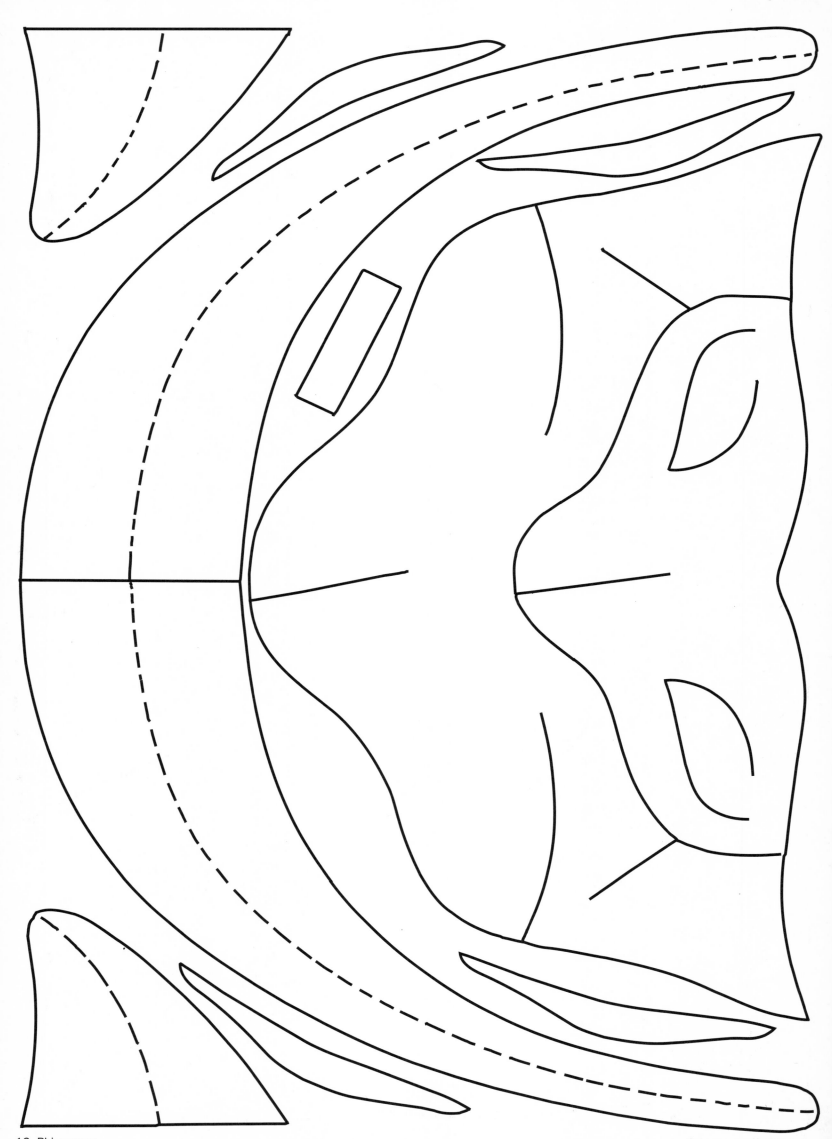

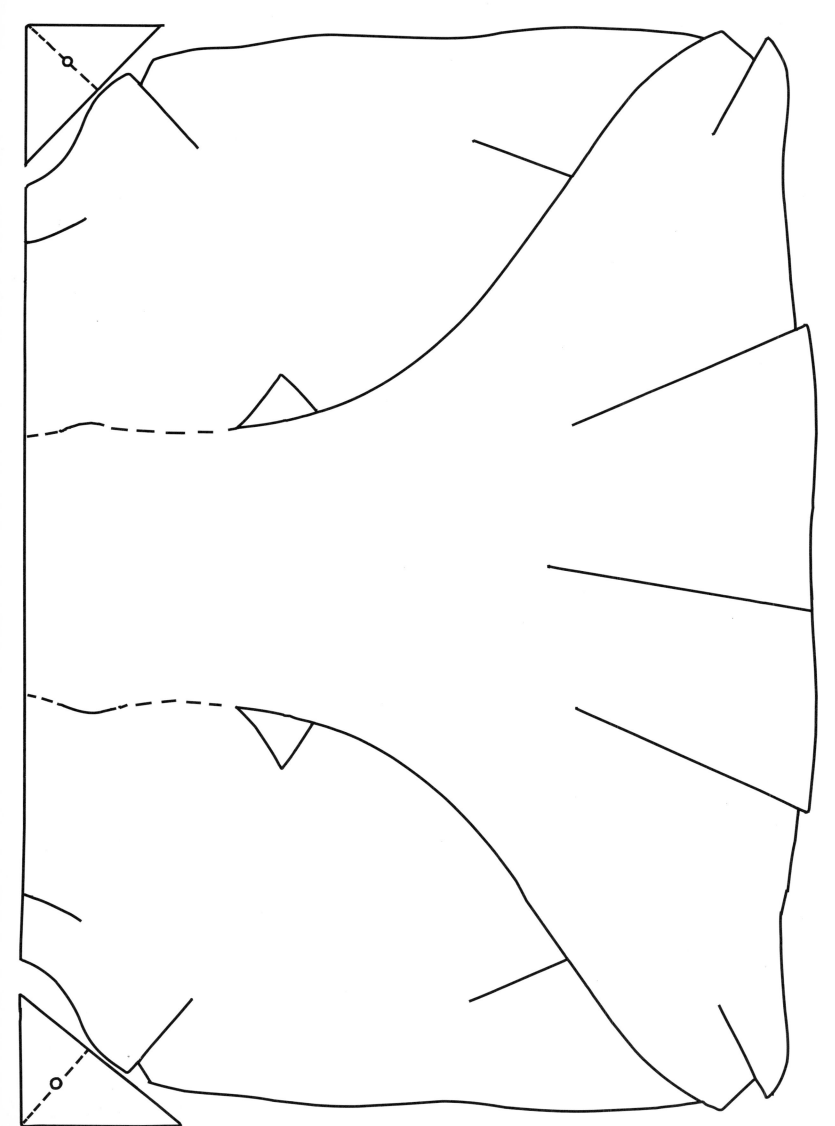

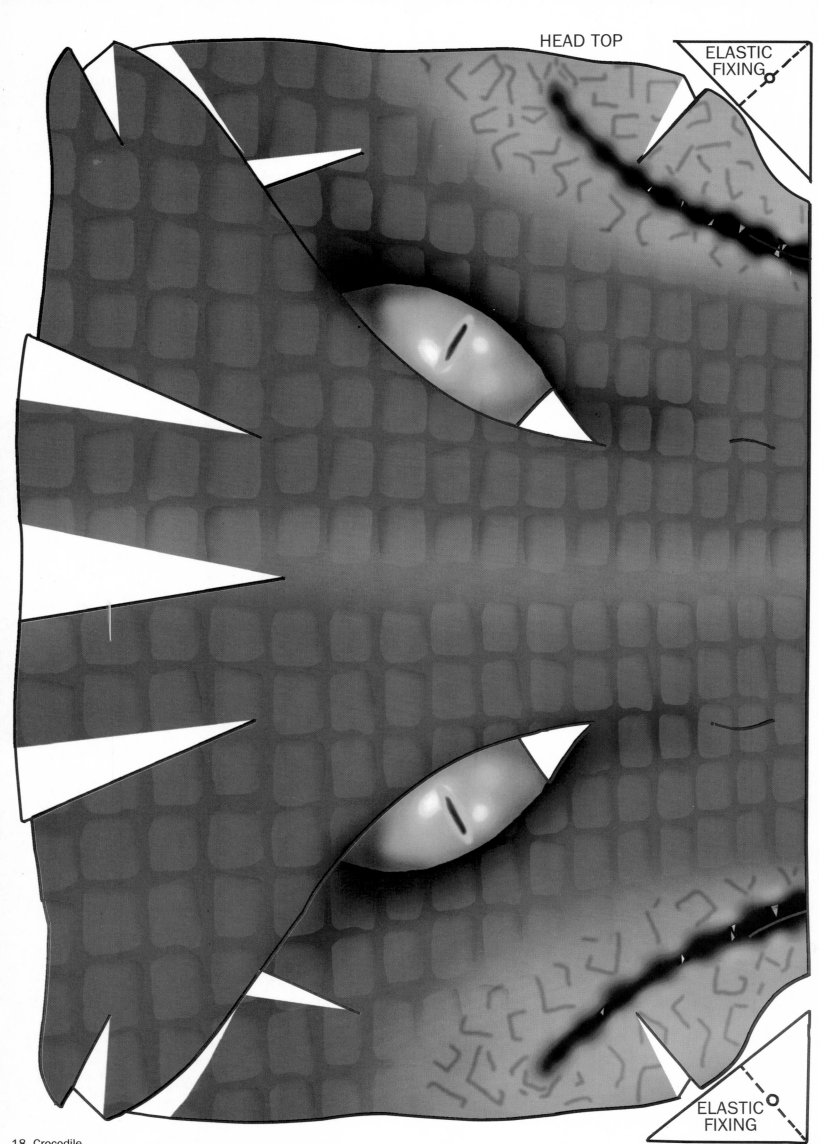

HEAD TOP

ELASTIC
FIXING

ELASTIC
FIXING

ELASTIC
FIXING

18 Crocodile

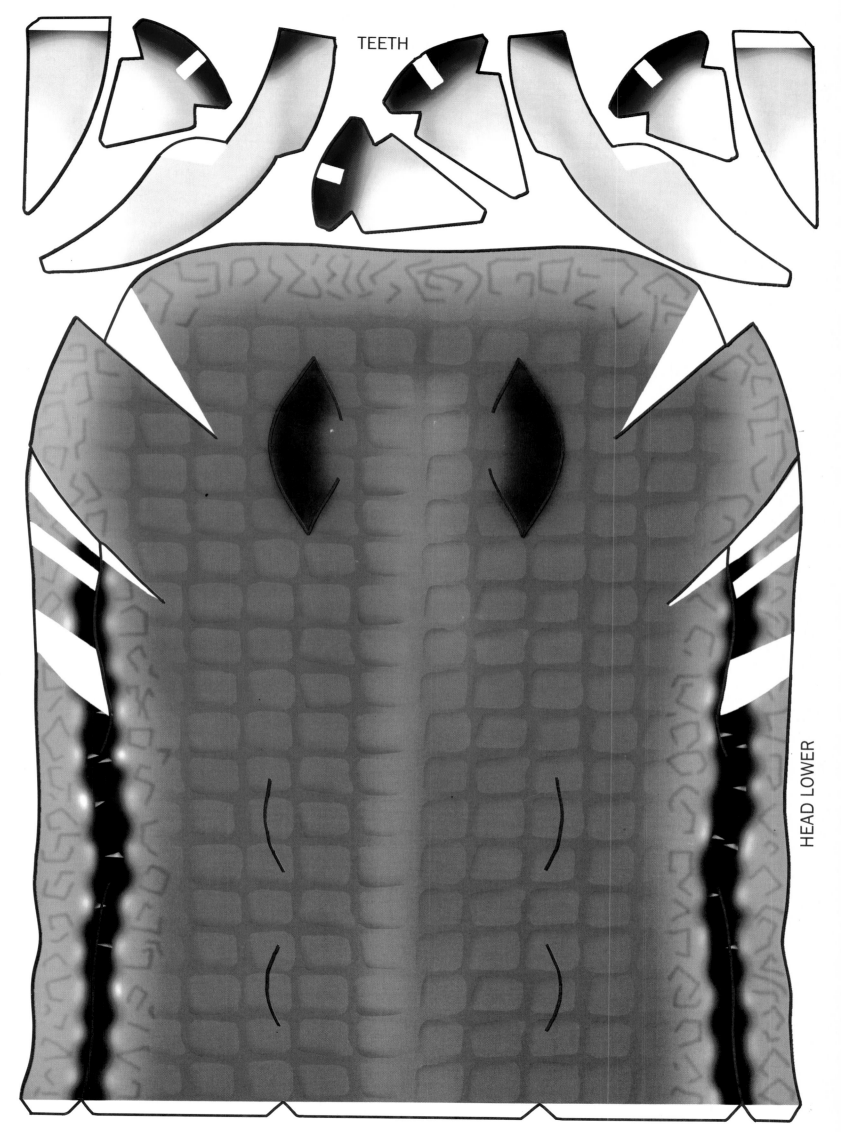

TEETH

HEAD LOWER

Crocodile 19

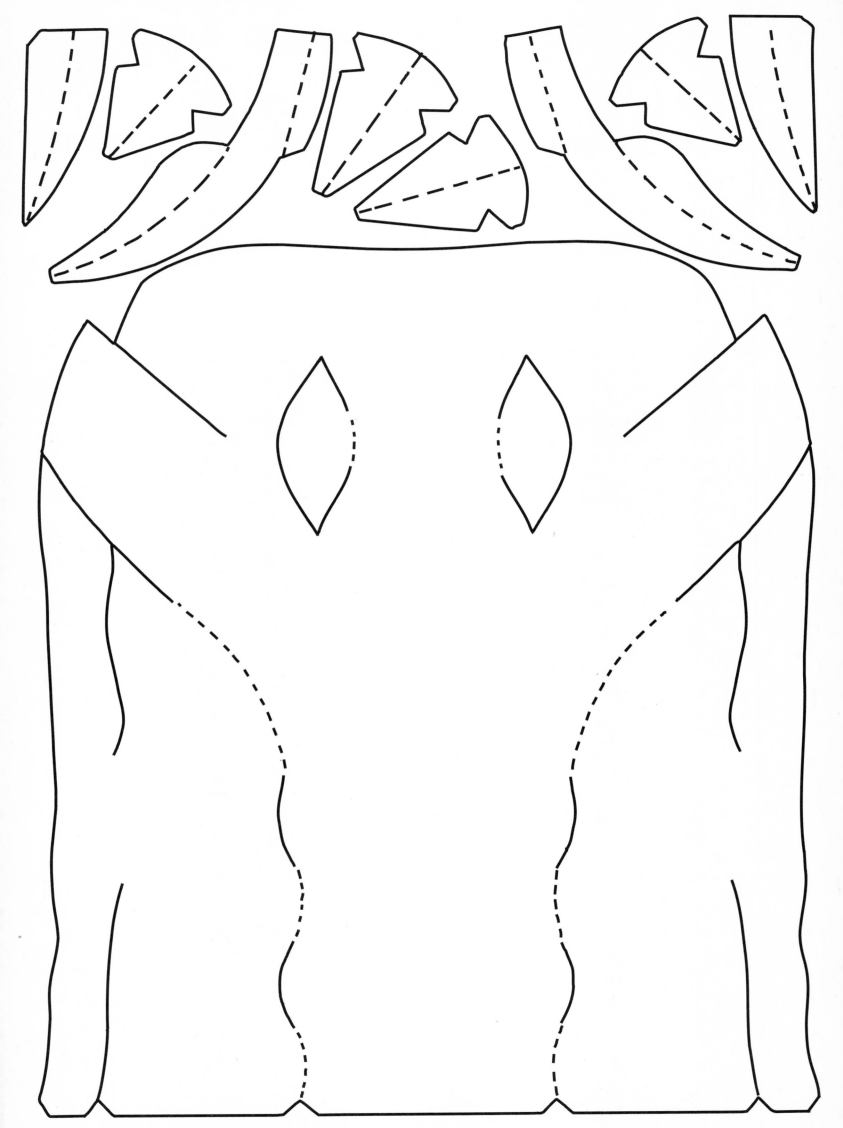

20 Crocodile

Lion 21

HEAD

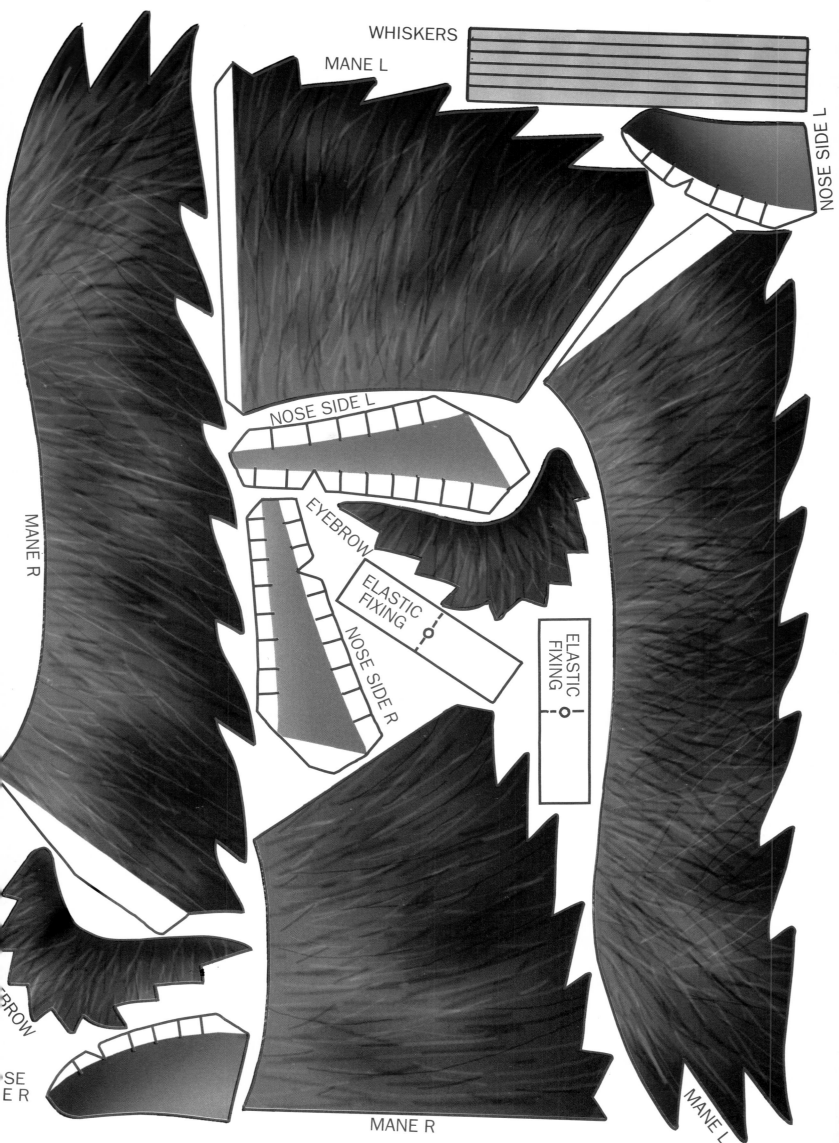

WHISKERS

MANE L

NOSE SIDE L

NOSE SIDE L

MANE R

EYEBROW

ELASTIC
FIXING

NOSE SIDE R

ELASTIC
FIXING

MANE R

MANE L

Lion 23

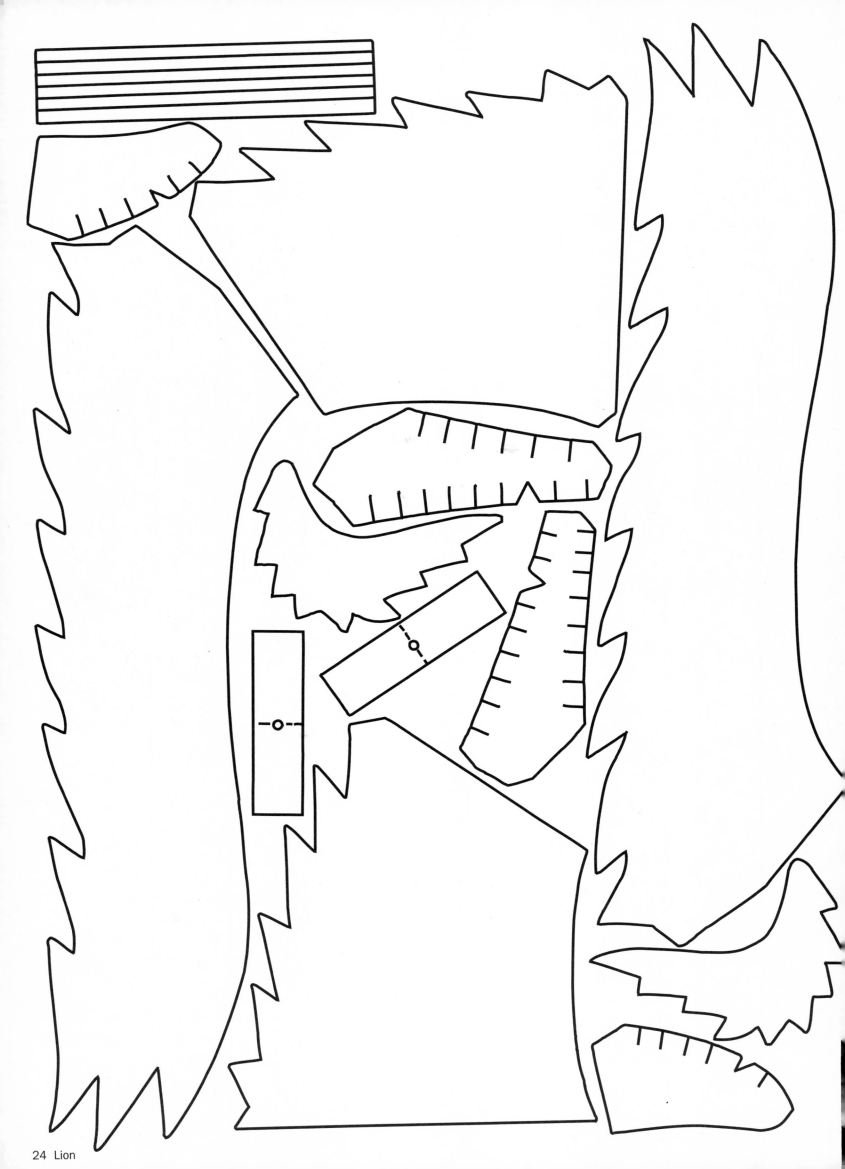

The Lion

Only a few hundred years ago, fearsome lions were common sights as they padded across Europe, Asia and Africa. Virtually all of the lions in the world today are confined to the savanna grasslands of Africa.

Sturdy and strong, the male is distinguished by his shaggy mane. He can measure up to 3 metres (10 ft) in length. Females do not have manes and are generally lighter in bodyweight. Both male and female lions are sandy coloured, which provides good camouflage against the dry landscape they live in. They have tails which end in a tuft.

Groups of lions are called prides. A pride may contain anything between four and 30 individuals and is ruled by a large male. Female lions are responsible for most of the hunting, for which the species is perhaps best known. For unlike the rest of the big cats, lions live in open grasslands, instead of among trees and dense vegetation, and move in large groups. Lions work together during a hunt, with breakaway groups driving whole herds of animals towards the remainder of the pride. A lion is both speedy and powerful, preying on animals as large as the zebra and wild ox. Even so, lions can be driven from feeding by hyenas.

The Human Hazard

The human population
is getting bigger all the time.
That means there is a greater demand
than ever for houses, factories and their
goods and foodstuffs from farms and fields.

As cities and towns expand and new
tracts of land are cultivated, the areas of
open countryside where wild animals thrive
are shrinking.

Many countries, particularly those with a
tropical climate, were once full of naturally
occurring forests which made safe homes for
scores of different creatures. These forests are
being cut down for timber, farmland and other
human activities, leaving many animals without
shelter or food. Scientists believe that the
clearance of these forests may also cause
changes in the climate.

Temperate countries like Britain used to be
full of marshes which were home to many
different mammals, birds and insects. Many
marshes have now been drained for farmland,
dramatically reducing the numbers of marsh-
dwelling species. Wild animals cannot choose
to move. If their habitat disappears, they die –
sometimes a whole species becomes extinct.

As well as destroying native habitats, humans
present other hazards to wildlife. Chemical
poisoning of even the largest animals often
takes place as a result of farmers spraying their
crops with pesticides; poisoned insects are
eaten by birds and other animals, who in turn
are eaten by larger animals with disastrous
effects. The seas have become polluted with oil
and chemicals which have been pumped out of
factories on the coast, or via rivers if they are
inland, which carried them into the sea. Some
factories also produce 'acid rain': when it rains
the chemicals in the smoke fall on to trees and
into rivers, damaging both trees and fish and
affecting other wildlife in the locality.

What can I do?

Every little effort helps wildlife, right across the world.

● Make sure that mum uses ecologically friendly soap powders to ease the pollution in rivers and seas.

● Choose products with the minimum amount of packaging. Unnecessary plastic packaging causes pollution while it is being made and makes excess litter.

● Wear second-hand clothes with pride. The fewer garments that are made, the less the pollution caused in manufacture - decreasing the ensuing threat to animals.

● If you eat tuna fish, make sure that it has been caught by rod and line instead of in drag nets which can also kill dolphins. Most tins are marked if they are 'dolphin friendly'.

● Recycle wherever you can. It is important to remember, however, that the environment is far better off if there is no demand for bottles, plastics and cans in the first place. Even the process of recycling causes damage to the world's resources.

Humans have always hunted animals for food. Today's sophisticated weapons, however, give us the advantage, and animals have little chance of escape. Hunters have relentlessly pursued some species, earning high prices for their horns or fur. Many countries have outlawed the hunting of certain animals. Those who are prepared to defy the law are known as poachers.

How to Make the Masks

ASK AN ADULT TO HELP YOU AND TAKE CARE WHEN USING SHARP KNIVES AND SCISSORS.

You will need:
▷ Small pair of sharp scissors or a craft knife with renewable blades;
▷ a ballpoint pen that has run out of ink (to make the creases);
▷ a small tube of contact adhesive glue (the sort that is put onto each surface to be stuck);
▷ carpenter's water-soluble glue (often referred to as PVA glue);
▷ some lengths of black or white cord elastic to secure the masks around the head.

Remove the model pages from the book. Read the instructions and look at the drawings to ensure you understand the assembly stages before starting to cut the parts. If you are not sure, go back over the instructions.

Work in a well-lit area where you can leave your model parts without them being damaged. Use a plastic cutting board or a thick sheet of cardboard to protect furniture.

You will find the cutting lines around the colour areas in a solid black line. Where the colour is very dark, the cutting lines are in white so that they are clearly visible. Try to cut to the edge of the black or white lines so that you will not see fragments of them on the finished mask.

The cutting lines are on the coloured side of the cardboard. On the reverse of each sheet, we have marked grey outlines (but do not use these for cutting lines) and dotted lines. These dotted lines show you where to fold the card. They have been positioned on the reverse so that they will not be visible on the finished masks. Put in the creases from the reverse.

Cut all solid lines. Crease all dotted lines.

Before you cut, double check that you are doing it correctly. Once you have cut, there is no going back. Only cut out and crease the parts as you need them in assembly - do not cut out all the pieces at once as you may then find it more difficult to follow the instructions.

Cutting Instructions

Use scissors where possible. If you need to use a craft knife, please ask an adult to do it for you – or to supervise you while you do it.

If using a craft knife, do not use blunt blades. Never place your hands or fingers in the line of your cut – always keep them to the side in case the blade slips. Try not to cut alongside plastic rulers or set squares – use steel edges instead (blades can catch the edge of plastic and run across onto the hand). Cut slowly along the solid black lines and press just firmly enough to cut through the card.

Don't forget to cut the small slits on the glue flaps where marked – these will enable you to curve pieces to shape.

Creasing Instructions

Crease each part as required after it has been cut out. Use the ballpoint pen to make the creases by running its nib along the dotted line gently to make a mark, and then going over it again to make a deeper crease. Try this on a piece of scrap paper first to see how it works.

Gluing Instructions

Do not apply glue straight from the tube. Use a strip of thick card like a narrow brush to spread the glue exactly where it is needed on the white glue areas. Use these areas line up the parts before pressing them into place. Take your time, don't rush, and check every step first.

Left and Right refers to the mask as worn on the face.

Bear Mask
(see pages 9-12)

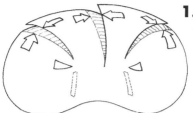

1. Overlap and glue the three long cuts in the Head as arrowed. They make the Head curve.

2. The Mouth must curve inwards as arrowed to form a concave shape. Overlap and glue to shape.

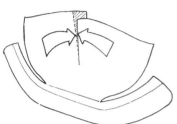

3. Continue to curve the Mouth to shape as shown at A. Fold and curve the crease at B in the strip. Gently work around its length so that each end can be folded flat and glue down at C each side. This strip forms the lip of the Bear.

4. Note how the glued under flaps line up with the top edge of the Mouth as arrowed. Glue each side down in position.

5. Glue the Mouth to each side of the lower part of the head as arrowed at A. Ensure it is central. Check that the central crease in the edge of the Mouth at B is folded evenly all around. Glue the two halves of the Teeth together, and note the small central

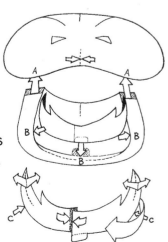

flap. Curve the Teeth to shape. Glue them into the Mouth using the small central flap and glue along their edges as arrowed at C.

6. The mask should now look like this.

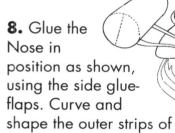

7. Glue the two halves of the Nose Tip together, and fold over the small outer glue-flaps as arrowed. Curve the Nose to shape, fold its glue-flaps under on each side. Glue the Nose Tip in position as shown, and line up each side at A.

8. Glue the Nose in position as shown, using the side glue-flaps. Curve and shape the outer strips of the Ears as arrowed. Curve them inwards and glue in position at A. Glue Ears in position to inside top of Head, placing the inner edges about 30mm (1.25 inches) inside the curved cuts, as marked at B.

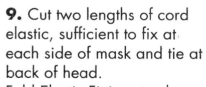

9. Cut two lengths of cord elastic, sufficient to fix at each side of mask and tie at back of head. Fold Elastic Fixings to shape. Thread elastic through hole as shown. Pull elastic so that knot is inside flaps, and glue flaps together. Glue Fixings to inside of mask in positions as shown. Tie elastic to comfortable fit with mask in position.

Rhino Mask
(see pages 13-16)

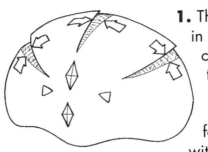

1. The three long cuts in the Head make it curve. Note the two diamond shaped centre cut-outs, each with four flaps. Starting with the centre cut, overlap and glue the three centre cuts as arrowed.

Cut two lengths of cord elastic, sufficient to fix at each side of mask and tie at back of head. Fold elastic fixings to shape. Thread elastic through hole and knot as shown. Pull elastic through so that knot is inside flaps, and glue together. Glue fixings to inside of mask in position as shown. Tie elastic to comfortable fit with mask in position.

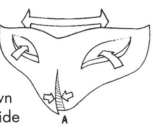

2. Separate the Upper Jaw from the Lower Jaw by cutting along the white line. Overlap and glue the Upper Jaw as shown at A. Push in nostrils each side as shown.

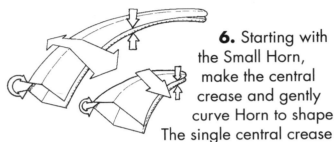

6. Starting with the Small Horn, make the central crease and gently curve Horn to shape. The single central crease gives them strength and shape. Match parts and glue together along curved edges. Apply glue sparingly along edges of one part only, wiping off excess when almost dry. Repeat for Large Horn.

3. Overlap and glue the centre cut in the Lower Jaw at B. Follow with the cuts at C each side, and then D each side. These gluings pull the Lower Jaw into shape.

7. Assemble each Ear as shown. Pull side strips of each Ear gently into position as arrowed and glue. Glue lower edges of Right and Left ears behind top of Head as arrowed, lining up with the long cut each side at A. Curve and glue each pair of Eyelids in position as arrowed at B.

4. Glue Upper Jaw centrally under lower edge of Head. Glue Tie Strip to centre position as arrowed.

Glue each Horn in position using the central flaps. The flaps go up inside the Horns. Put a small amount of glue along the inside edge of each Horn and press flaps to the inside of the Horns from behind the mask.

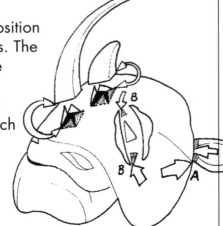

5. Turn the mask over. Glue Lower Jaw in position to Head and Upper Jaw as arrowed, lining up at corners of nostrils as arrowed at A each side. Glue Tie Strip to Lower Jaw as shown at B, leaving a small mouth opening.

Crocodile Mask
(see pages 17-20)

1. Overlap and glue Top and Lower parts of the Head together. Ensure they line up exactly.

2. The cuts in the back of the Top Head, and at the sides, make it curve to shape. Start with the centre cut. Overlap and glue at A. Repeat at B each side. Do the same at C in the corners. Overlap and glue the inner cuts at D each side, and follow with the cuts at E each side. Bring the head together and glue each side at F. Curve and fold the head as arrowed. Note how the small curved cuts and creases further shape the Head. Ensure that each central shaped crease is folded evenly to shape the Head and keep it rigid.

3. Push in the nostrils. Continue to fold and curve the Head as arrowed. Glue each of the sides at A, and the front section as arrowed at B.

4. Fold and shape the Teeth along their centre crease as arrowed. Glue the smaller of the Front Teeth in position as arrowed each side at A. Fold and glue down the small flap on each of the larger Teeth, as arrowed at B. Line up and glue the larger Teeth in position as arrowed and under the front edge of the Head at C.

5. Fold the back Teeth to shape as shown. Teeth lock in position in the rear mouth cut as shown. Spot glue as arrowed to keep them in place.

6. Cut two lengths of cord elastic, sufficient to fix at each side of mask and tie at back of head. Fold Elastic Fixings to shape. Thread elastic through hole as shown. Pull elastic so that knot is inside flaps, and glue flaps together. Glue Fixings to inside of mask in positions as shown. Tie elastic to comfortable fit with mask in position.

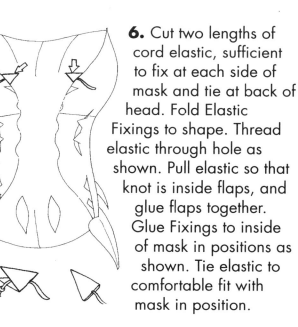

Lion Mask
(see pages 21-24)

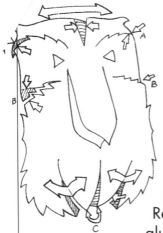

1. The three cuts along the top of the Head make it curve. Overlap and glue the central cut. Overlap and glue the shapes cuts each side at A. The serrated shape then stands proud of the background. Repeat the overlapping and gluing at B each side.
Note how the central Nose cut-out begins to stand out. Overlap and glue the central cut at C. This part curves outwards to form the Chin. The cuts each side curve inwards as arrowed. Overlap each side and glue behind each edge of the Chin.

2. The mask should now look like this. Note how the nose protrudes and the chin is formed to a rounded shape.

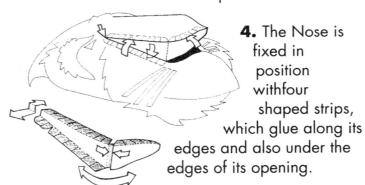

3. Curve and glue right and left Eyebrows in position as arrowed. When dry, they should be curved away from the head slightly to give added dimension. Glue the Whiskers in position as shown. Curve and shape them.

4. The Nose is fixed in position with four shaped strips, which glue along its edges and also under the edges of its opening.

Note how this part is glued in position. Glue the sides of the nose together as shown, then glue them in position as arrowed.

5. The Mane is glued together as shown. Note how the parts line up.

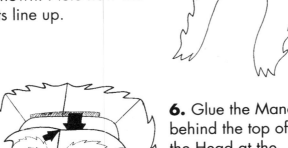

6. Glue the Mane behind the top of the Head at the centre point as arrowed. Bring the sides of the Mane in and glue them behind the edges of the Head as arrowed. Lock and glue the Mane into the cut-outs at A each side.

7. Cut two lengths of cord elastic, sufficient to fix at each side of mask and tie at back of head. Fold Elastic Fixings to shape. Thread elastic through hole as shown. Pull elastic so that knot is inside flaps, and glue flaps together. Glue Fixings to inside of mask in positions as shown.

Tie elastic to comfortable fit with mask in position.

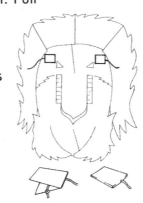

First published in Great Britain in 1995 by Parragon Book Service Ltd, Units 13-17, Avonbridge Trading Estate, Atlantic Road, Avonmouth, Bristol BS11 9QD.
© Parragon Book Service Ltd 1995.
All rights reserved. ISBN 0-7525-1071-1. Printed in Great Britain